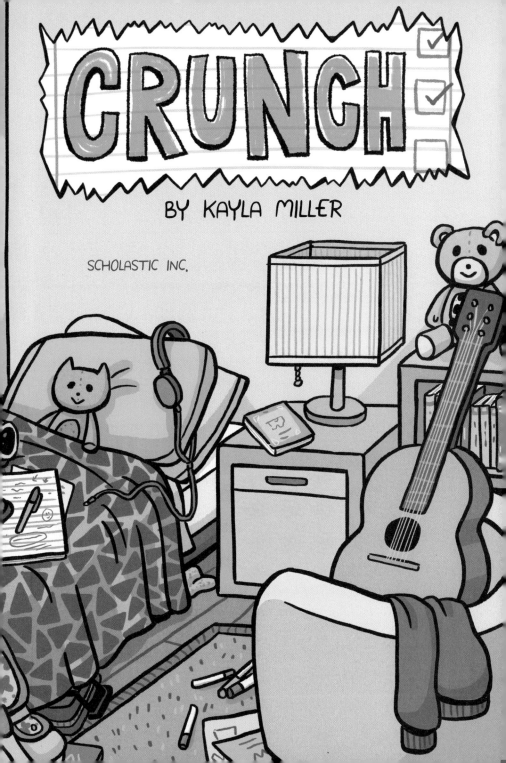

FOR THOSE OF US WHO NEED A BREAK. —KM

COLOR BY JESS LOME
LETTERING BY MICAH MYERS

ISBN 978-1-339-00601-7

12 11 10 9 8 7 6 5 4 3 2 1   23 24 25 26 27 28

Printed in the U.S.A.   40

First Scholastic printing, January 2023

The artist used Photoshop to create the digital illustrations for this book.

Typography by Stephanie Hays

1

2

9

ARE YOU OKAY, WILLOW?

I'M FINE...

IT'S JUST...MY PARENTS SIGNED ME UP FOR BERRY SCOUTS.

11

14

15

17

20

OKAY.

HAVE ANY OF YOU EVER GOTTEN A WARNING OR DETENTION OVER A DRESS-CODE VIOLATION?

I'VE NEVER HAD AN ISSUE.

NEITHER HAVE I.

I'VE NEVER GOTTEN A DETENTION, BUT I DID GET A "STERN WARNING" ABOUT ONE OF MY TOPS. I'VE KEPT A SPARE CARDIGAN IN MY LOCKER EVER SINCE.

YOU NEVER TOLD ME THAT! WHICH TOP?

CHARTREUSE WITH DAISIES. THE VINTAGE ONE.

GASP!

RIDICULOUS! I *LOVE* THAT SHIRT!

HMM...DOESN'T SEEM LIKE A LOT OF HOMEWORK IS GETTING DONE TODAY.

STRANGE, CONSIDERING SOMEONE HAS A BERRY SCOUT MEETING THIS AFTERNOON AND ASKED TO GO TO A FRIEND'S HOUSE TOMORROW.

MESSAGE RECEIVED. HOMEWORK SEQUENCE INITIATED.

HI THERE! ARE THOSE OUR NEW BERRY SCOUTS I SEE?

I'M TODD, THIS BUSH'S ELDERBERRY—OR THIS TROOP'S SCOUT LEADER, FOR THOSE NOT YET HIP TO BERRY SCOUT LINGO.

HELLO, I'M OLIVE, AND THIS IS WILLOW.

VERY GOOD, OLIVE...

OR SHOULD I SAY, **WILLOW**.

TODAY WE'LL BE LEARNING HOW TO DEAL WITH ONE OF THE MOST COMMON INJURIES THAT HAPPEN DURING HIKES: SPRAINED ANKLES.

LONG STORY SHORT: YOU'RE GOING TO WANT TO REST, PUT SOME ICE ON IT, MAYBE WRAP IT IN A BANDAGE DEPENDING ON HOW MUCH IT HURTS, AND PROP THAT BABY UP ON A PILLOW.

BUT IF YOU'RE IN THE MIDDLE OF A HIKE, YOU PROBABLY DON'T HAVE A TON OF ICE PACKS AND PILLOWS HANDY.

WHICH IS WHY TODAY WE'LL BE PRACTICING—

THE TWO-PERSON CARRY!

THAT'S RIGHT! WE'RE GONNA DO A TWO-PERSON-CARRY RACE SO WE CAN ALL LEARN HOW TO GET AN INJURED FRIEND TO SAFETY.

41

43

45

50

GOOD MORNING! WE SORT OF HAVE A FAVOR TO ASK YOU—

BUT HOPEFULLY A FUN FAVOR?

WE WANT TO PROVE THAT SOME OF THE DRESS-CODE RULES ARE UNFAIR, AND SINCE SOME OF YOU HAVE BEEN AFFECTED DIRECTLY...

...WE WERE WONDERING IF YOU'D HELP US PUT ON A FASHION SHOW!

WE HAVE TO RUN IT BY MS. LIN, BUT OUR IDEA IS THAT YOU COULD WEAR OUTFITS THAT YOU DON'T THINK YOU SHOULD HAVE GOTTEN IN TROUBLE FOR AND WALK THE RUNWAY AT A STUDENT COUNCIL MEETING.

WE *LOVE* FASHION SHOWS.

SOUNDS LIKE FUN.

I'M IN.

WHATEVER.

CLICK
CLICK
CLACK

59

65

79

OPERATION FASHION SHOW IS A GO!

WHEN?

NEXT THURSDAY, AFTER SCHOOL.

BRING YOUR OUTFITS TO CHANGE INTO AFTER CLASS— LIV AND I WILL TAKE CARE OF THE REST.

CAN I STILL WALK THE RUNWAY IF I HAVEN'T HAD ANY RUN-INS WITH THE FASHION POLICE?

97

THAT WAS A VALIANT EFFORT FOR A PAIR OF NEW BLUEBERRIES,

BUT I THINK YOU COULD DO WITH A LITTLE MORE PRACTICE.

I'M SURE YOU'LL GET YOUR FIRST-AID BADGE WHEN THE TEST ROLLS BACK AROUND NEXT YEAR.

ALL RIGHT, LET'S SEE HOW TO TREAT AN ALLERGIC REACTION FROM TARA AND ANTHONY.

HEY, WILLOW...

I'M REALLY SORRY WE DIDN'T GET OUR MERIT BADGES. I KNOW I SHOULD HAVE SPENT MORE TIME STUDYING YOUR NOTES. I HOPE YOU'RE NOT **BERRY** MAD AT ME?

IT'S OKAY. IT'S NOT LIKE I DID A **BERRY** GOOD JOB EITHER.

GIRLS! READY TO HEAD OUT?

DO YOU STILL WANT TO COME OVER AND WORK ON THE MOVIE TOMORROW?

SURE.

116

121

BEEP!

NEW MAIL

YAWN!

AND FINALLY, A LOOK THAT WOULD LEAVE THE FASHION POLICE SPEECHLESS...

SAWYER'S SPORTING RIPPED JEANS, BARE SHOULDERS, SUNGLASSES, **AND** A HAT INDOORS.

HOW MANY DETENTIONS IS THAT?

THAT WAS CERTAINLY ILLUMINATING... AND ENTERTAINING.

I DON'T SEE ANY REASON WHY YOU SHOULDN'T BE ALLOWED TO WEAR THESE CLOTHES TO SCHOOL.

WITH THE EXCEPTION OF SOME OF MR. MOORE'S ACCESSORIES. I THINK IT'S ABOUT TIME WE UPDATED OUR RULES A LITTLE.

SORRY. I DIDN'T MEAN TO LAUGH...

IT'S OKAY. IT **IS** SORT OF FUNNY.

IT MUST BE HARD TO MAKE SOMETHING **ACTUALLY** SCARY.

THINK ABOUT ALL THE BIG-BUDGET HORROR MOVIES THAT END UP BEING FUNNY WHEN THEY'RE TRYING TO BE SERIOUS.

TRYING TO BE SERIOUS...

KNOCK KNOCK

GOOD MORNING!

HEY, AUNT MOLLY!

ARE YOU SURE YOU WANT TO COME TO WORK WITH ME TODAY, SUGAR?

YOU WON'T GET A PAYCHECK.

YOU COULD ALWAYS PUT YOUR JAMMIES BACK ON AND HAVE A RELAXING MORNING INSTEAD OF SPENDING ALL DAY AT THE LIBRARY.

THAT'S WHAT I'D DO.

I NEED TO DO SOME RESEARCH—AND I WANT A PLACE WHERE I CAN WORK **UNDISTURBED** IF I'M GOING TO REWRITE MY MOVIE SCRIPT BY TOMORROW.

LET'S GO!

AT LEAST LET ME GRAB A CINNAMON ROLL FIRST!

159

DID YOU GET BITTEN BY A ZOMBIE AT BERRY SCOUTS OR SOMETHING?

PATOOIE!

I'M JUST THINKING ABOUT WILLOW. I'M GOING TO GIVE THE MAIN CHARACTER ROLE IN THE MOVIE TO AVA, BUT I WANT WILLOW TO HAVE SOMETHING TO DO SO SHE CAN FEEL INCLUDED.

CRAFT SERVICES!

WHAT DO YOU THINK, LIV? IS THE NEW FOOTAGE LOOKING GOOD?

IT LOOKS **GREAT.**

NOW ALL YOU HAVE TO DO IS FIGURE OUT HOW TO GET THE STOP-MOTION STUFF TO LOOK GOOD.

YOU KNOW WHO YOU SHOULD TALK TO?

CHANDA! SHE'S GOOD WITH CAMERAS.

THAT'S TRUE—SHE'S ALWAYS POSTING REALLY COOL GLAMOUR SHOTS OF BETH.

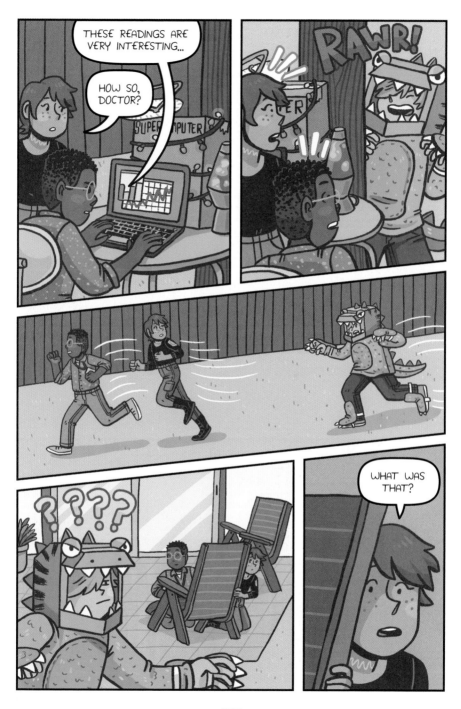

THAT WAS SO COOL!

TOP-NOTCH EMERGENCY TREATMENT, DOCTOR WILLOW. I MIGHT HAVE TO MAKE AN EXCEPTION AND LET YOU RETAKE YOUR FIRST-AID TEST.

REALLY? THANK YOU.

OUR NEXT BADGE IS FOR NATURE SKILLS. I WAS WONDERING IF YOU'D WANT TO PARTNER UP SINCE YOU KNOW ABOUT PLANTS AND STUFF?

AND SINCE OLIVE QUIT.

209

212

I'M SO GLAD EVERYONE COULD COME OUT TONIGHT—

—BUT I HOPE WE WRAP UP SOON. I'VE GOT ONE LAST APPOINTMENT I CAN'T MISS...

How "To Do" A To-Do List

When you've got a lot to do, it can feel overwhelming—but being organized can help! Here are some To-Do List tips on how to avoid the crunch and stay cool when things get busy.

Figure out your top priorities . . . and put them at the top of your list!
If you take care of the most important things first, the rest of your list will feel like a breeze!

Celebrate your accomplishments!
You don't need to have a dance party every time you get something done (though you totally could), but acknowledging your hard work in some way is a must. This can be as simple as marking your finished tasks with stickers.

Break big tasks down into smaller steps.
Big projects like cleaning your whole room (or writing and illustrating a whole book) might seem intimidating, but breaking them down into smaller tasks can make it more manageable. This also lets you pace yourself and tackle each step in your own time.

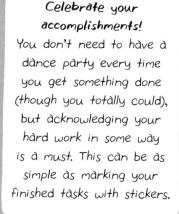

Don't forget to add some fun things to your list too! To-do lists don't have to be all work and no play. Taking breaks is really important, so why not schedule a walk outside, a call with a friend, or some time to devote to one of your hobbies?

Ask for help if you need it. Even when you have all your ducks in a row, sometimes there's just too many ducks! If there's no way you can manage all your goals on your own, it's better to ask for help and figure out your options before the last minute.

What Is Stop-Motion Animation?

Stop motion is an animation technique that uses a series of photographs in which the subject has been moved slightly between each image to create the illusion of movement when the images are shown in succession at a high speed. Technically, all film and animation is a series of still images, but stop-motion animation allows artists to use this fact to their advantage and create footage where inanimate objects appear to be moving on their own, or beings seem able to do things that they wouldn't normally be able to do—such as making someone look like they're hovering by taking multiple pictures of them mid-jump. Stop motion has been used throughout film history in a myriad of ways, and the limits of the technique are defined only by an individual's imagination . . . and the available time and resources.

The method can be done with clay, posable puppets, paper, people, found objects, or any subject that can be arranged and photographed. The number of photos needed to create this effect varies, as does the number of images in other forms of video, but the most common for TV and film is 24 FPS (frames per second). This means that there are 24 images in each second of video! So a minute of animation at 24 FPS contains 1440 pictures. A lot of animation is "shot on twos," which means each image is shown for two frames, so there are 12 frames per second. Some animation is shot on threes or fours, but even at that lower frame rate, the animators still need to create hundreds of images for one minute of animation—and a whole lot more for an entire movie or show!

This might sound pretty complicated, but you can still make your own simple stop-motion animation at home just like Chanda, Beth, and Olive did! All you need to do is set up a camera in a way so that it won't move between pictures—a tripod works best, but if you're using a phone or tablet, a stand will work. Then, start taking photos of something! Whatever you choose as your subject, move it just a tiny little bit between each picture. The smaller the changes between each frame, the more fluid the movements will look in the finished animation. Once you have all of your images, turn them into video using a video-editing software. There are free apps for this, and some computers even come with programs already installed. Just ask a tech-savvy adult to help you get set up.

Acknowledgments

I want to express my appreciation for everyone on Team Click whose hard work helped another story exit my head and become a book! Thanks to my editor, Mary, and my agent, Elizabeth, for their continued enthusiasm for Olive and her friends. Thank you to Jess for another round of coloring, collaboration, and companionship. Thanks to Steph for designing with an attention to detail and for being so dedicated to smoothing out all the wrinkles along the way. And thank you to Lor for lending their lettering skills to the project and helping these chatty kids speak up. It's a pleasure to work with all of you!

I'd also like to extend gratitude to my friends and family for their support. As the people in my life know, Olive's struggles in this book are not unfamiliar to me, and it's nice to have loved ones who check in and make sure I don't Crunch too hard. Mom, Dad, Grandpa, Karen, Will, Kristina, Gabe, and Lish—thank you for being there for me. Special thanks to K and Tyler for sharing your animation expertise; I'm lucky to have such smart and talented pals. And lastly, Jeffrey...I'm so happy to have you by my side in life—and quite literally by my side when writing so I can ask you how to spell things.

—KAYLA

Photo by Jeffrey Canino

KAYLA MILLER is the *New York Times* bestselling creator of four previous graphic novels, *Click, Camp, Act,* and *Clash,* and the coauthor of the Besties series. An author-illustrator and cartoonist with a BFA from the University of the Arts in Philadelphia, Kayla lives and works in New York.